Sing in Praise

Sing in Praise

A Collection of the Best Loved Hymns

Stories of the Hymns and Music Arrangements by

Opal Wheeler

Illustrated by

Marjorie Torrey

New York, E. P. Dutton and Company, Inc., 1946

CONTENTS
STORIES

Onward, Christian Soldiers

O God, Our Help in Ages Past   13

Faith of Our Fathers   16

A Mighty Fortress Is Our God   21

Rock of Ages   24

Jerusalem, the Golden   28

All Hail the Power of Jesus' Name   32

My Faith Looks Up to Thee   36

Now the Day Is Over   40

Abide with Me   44

Fairest Lord Jesus   48

Come, Thou Almighty King   52

Blest Be the Tie That Binds   56

Dear Lord And Father Of Mankind   73

Christ The Lord Is Risen To-day   77

From Greenland's Icy Mountains   80

Nearer, My God, to Thee   84

Holy, Holy, Holy!   88

O Worship the King   92

CONTENTS

MUSIC

Onward, Christian Soldiers   10

O God Our Help in Ages Past   12

Faith of Our Fathers   18

A Mighty Fortress Is Our God   20

Rock of Ages   26

Jerusalem the Golden   30

All Hail the Power of Jesus' Name   34

My Faith Looks Up to Thee   38

Now the Day Is Over   42

Abide with Me   46

Fairest Lord Jesus   50

Come, Thou Almighty King   54

Blest Be the Tie That Binds   58

Children of the Heavenly King   60

Saviour, Teach Me, Day by Day   62

Heavenly Father, Send Thy Blessing   64

Jesus, Tender Shepherd, Hear Me   66

I Think When I Read That Sweet Story   68

Morning Thanks   70

Dear Lord and Father of Mankind   72

Christ the Lord Is Risen To-day   76

From Greenland's Icy Mountains   82

Nearer, My God, to Thee   86

Holy, Holy, Holy!   90

O Worship the King   94

Sing in Praise

SABINE BARING - GOULD paced the floor of his small cold Yorkshire study, stopping now and then for a bit of warmth at the low grate fire. He was anxious, and well he might be, for tomorrow was Whit Monday, when all the children of the nearby villages would gather together for a very special celebration.

His own little flock would join in the festivities, and would march to the next school to meet the many children gathered there. Young pastor Baring-Gould loved his Sunday School more than anything else in all the world. But the boys were mischievous, very mischievous, indeed, and to get them to the next village, and in order, was a great problem.

A frown wrinkled the brow of the gifted young writer, and on he paced, lost in thought. If only the boys could be kept busy, all would go well.

Suddenly the pacing stopped short. A marching song would be all that was needed! Eagerly the young pastor searched, but there was none to be found. Then he must write one himself, he decided.

Through the long night hours he sat at his small table, pen in hand, but the words would not come. Then, just as the daylight began to steal into his cold bare room, lines rushed into his mind, and eagerly he wrote them down:

> "Onward, christian soldiers,
> Marching as to war."

It was not long before the children came bounding in, and hearing the martial words to a made up tune, they learned the lines speedily and were off through the beautiful English country lanes, joyously chanting the fine new song as they tramped proudly along.

Not once did they break ranks as they marched past bright green meadows and hills dotted with sheep, their victorious song ringing out ever more gladsome in the fresh spring air: "Onward, christian soldiers, marching as to war."

The noted English musician, Sir Arthur Sullivan, visiting at the old Dorsetshire estate of a good friend, came upon the verses written by Baring-Gould one day, and carried away by the martial spirit of the lines, decided to set them to music at once.

Gathering the members of the family together in the beautiful little chapel, he quickly composed a melody at the old harmonium, teaching the lines, one at a time, to the eager group.

Soon they were all singing the lively, jubilant song that we are still singing today—the cheerful, moving, marching hymn, "Onward, Christian Soldiers."

Onward, Christian Soldiers

SABINE BARING-GOULD   ARTHUR SULLIVAN

1. On-ward, Chris-tian sol - diers, March-ing as to war, With the cross of
2. Like a might-y ar - my Moves the Church of God; Broth-ers, we are
3. On-ward, then, ye peo - ple! Join our hap-py throng! Blend with ours your

Je - sus Go - ing on be - fore! Christ, the roy - al Mas - ter
tread - ing Where the saints have trod; We are not di - vi - ded,
voic - es In the tri - umph song! Glo - ry, laud, and hon - our,

Leads a-gainst the foe; For-ward in - to bat - tle,_ See, His ban-ners go.
All one bod-y we, One in hope and doc-trine, One in char-i - ty.
Un - to Christ, the King; This through count-less a - ges_ Men and an-gels sing.

On - ward, Chris-tian sol - diers,_ March-ing as to_ war,

With the cross of Je - sus Go - ing on be - fore!

O God Our Help in Ages Past

ISAAC WATTS

WILLIAM CROFT

1. O God, our help in a - ges past, Our
2. Be - fore the hills in or - der stood, Or
3. A thou - sand a - ges in Thy sight Are
4. Time, like an ev - er - roll - ing stream, Bears
5. O God, our help in a - ges past, Our

hope for years to come, Our shel - ter from the
earth re - ceived her frame, From ev - er - last - ing
like an eve - ning gone; Short as the watch that
all its sons a - way; Then fly, for - got - ten,
hope for years to come, Be Thou our Guide while

storm - y blast, And our e - ter - nal home.
Thou art God, To end - less years the same.
ends the night, Be - fore the ris - ing sun.
as a dream Dies at the o - p'ning day.
life shall last, And our e - ter - nal home.

O GOD, OUR HELP IN AGES PAST

THE busy day in the Southampton home of the Watts family was over at last, and fair haired Isaac was glad to crawl into a warm nook close to the glowing hearth, for a cold damp chill had crept over the old house.

It was time for family prayers, and setting his square rimmed glasses firmly on his nose, Schoolmaster Watts reached for the big Book.

Just as the solemn reading began, a light scratching sounded in the low pile of wood at his side. Opening his blue eyes quickly, Isaac watched a sharp nosed little gray mouse run swiftly up the bell rope to the rafter overhead, there to sit watching the scene below with round, beady black eyes.

Merry laughter rang through the house and the prayers stopped suddenly.

"Isaac!" reprimanded father Watts sternly.

"See,—a mouse at prayers!" exclaimed Isaac, adding solemnly: "A mouse, for want of better stairs, climbed up a rope to say his prayers."

There were always services in the church on Sunday, and Isaac liked to listen, but when it came time for the chanting of the psalms, he could never sit still.

"Why could there not be real music in the church?" he asked one Sunday on the way home. "A melody with words to sing would be far better than the chanting."

Schoolmaster Watts turned abruptly to his son.

"Then give us something better, young man," he commanded.

It did not take long for Isaac to get started, and that very afternoon he was hard at work and when the next Sunday arrived, there was a beautiful hymn for the people to sing. Everyone was delighted and called for more music from the young composer.

Nothing could stop Isaac now, and every Sunday for two whole years there was a fresh hymn for the congregation, until a whole book was filled with his lovely songs.

This was the very beginning of hymn singing in England, and in Scotland, too, so that Isaac Watts later became known as the Father of Hymnody.

He especially liked to make verses for children and for some mischievous, care free boys of an Englishman he wrote: "How doth the busy little bee improve each shining hour?" and one of the loveliest cradle songs ever written:

> "Hush, my babe, lie still and slumber,
> Holy angels guard thy bed;
> Heavenly blessings without number,
> Gently falling on thy head."

Isaac Watts's poetry never stopped, and when his dearest wish came true and he went to preach to the people in one of the largest churches in London, he kept right on writing beautiful hymns, over six hundred coming from his pen.

His fame spread across the ocean to America, Benjamin Franklin so liking his songs, that the very first book to come from his press was "Watts Psalms and Hymn Tunes."

Watts loved Bible stories, especially the one telling of the help that Moses received from God in ages past, when he escaped from the Egyptians and passed unharmed through the waters of the Red Sea.

And just two hundred years ago, he came to write the fine strong hymn that we like to sing so well: "O God, Our Help in Ages Past," set to a simple, hardy melody by the English musician, William Croft.

FAITH OF OUR FATHERS

LONG years ago, in the early days of our country, when no sounds broke the stillness of forest and lake but those of Indians and wild animals, there came to our shores a weary little band of men and women and children who called themselves Pilgrims.

They were lonely folk, for they had left behind them much that they held dear in their homeland. But the days there had become ever more dangerous, with fathers and brothers thrown into dungeons for daring to worship God in their own way.

And so across angry waters to the strange new land of America they had fled,—homeless, friendless, and alone. New dangers and sickness caused many an anxious heart to beat faster, and the members of the little band grew steadily less, but still from every rough log cabin, grateful prayers for freedom arose night and day.

And back in the land they had left behind them, the courageous young Englishman, Frederick Faber, needing new hymns that could be understood by the simple country folk of his small church, wrote for them the stirring "Faith of Our Fathers."

In this beautiful song, Faber told of the courage of the fearless Pilgrims, who, before they left their homeland, dared to worship as their hearts bade them, in spite of dungeon, fire, and sword.

The words of this challenging hymn were set to music by the English musician and organist, Henri Frederick Hemi, later changed a little by James Walton.

Never can we sing this noble, glowing tribute to our forefathers without a little prayer of thanksgiving for the brave men who fought so valiantly to give us the thing we hold most dear,—freedom to worship as we please.

> Faith of our fathers, living still,
> In spite of dungeon, fire, and sword;
> Oh, how our hearts beat high with joy
> Whene'er we hear that glorious word.
> Faith of our fathers, holy faith,
> We will be true to Thee till death.

Faith of Our Fathers

FREDERICK W. FABER

Arranged by J. G. WALTON

1. Faith of our fa - thers! liv - ing still In spite of
2. Our fa - thers, chained in pris - ons dark, Were still in
3. Faith of our fa - thers! we will love Both friend and

dun - geon, fire, and sword: O how our hearts beat
heart and con - science free: How sweet would be their
foe in all our strife: And preach thee, too, as

high with joy When-e'er we hear that glo - rious word!
chil - dren's fate, If they, like them, could die for thee!
love knows how, By kind - ly words and vir - tuous life:

Faith of our fa - thers! ho - ly faith!

will be true to thee till death!

A Mighty Fortress Is Our God

MARTIN LUTHER   MARTIN LUTHER

1. A might-y fort-ress is__ our God, A bul-wark nev-er fail - ing, Our
2. Did we in our__ own strength con-fide, Our striv-ing would be los - ing, Were
3. And though this world, with dev - ils fill'd, Should threat-en to un-do__ us; We
4. That word a - bove all earth - ly pow'rs, No thanks to them, a - bid - eth; The

help-er He__ a - mid__ the flood Of mor-tal ills pre - vail - ing: For
not the right man on__ our side The man of God's own choos__ ing: Dost
will not fear,- for God hath will'd His truth to tri - umph through us: The
Spir - it and__ the gifts are ours Through Him who with us sid - eth: Let

still our an - cient foe Doth seek to work us woe, His craft and pow'r are__
ask who that may be? Christ Je - sus, it is He; Lord Sa - ba - oth His
prince of dark - ness, grim, We trem-ble not for him, His rage we can en -
goods and kin - dred go, This mor - tal life al - so, The bod - y they may

great, And, armed with cru - el hate, On earth is not his e - qual.
Name, From age to age__ the same, And He must win the__ bat - tle.
dure, For lo! his doom is sure, One lit - tle word shall fell__ him.
kill: God's truth a - bid - eth still, His king - dom is for - ev - er.

A MIGHTY FORTRESS IS OUR GOD

ON St. Martin's eve in chill November, on the edge of the Black Forest, there was born in the earthen floored cottage of mine worker Luther, a fair little blue-eyed boy, and his parents called him Martin.

There was little to give the golden haired child, for nowhere in all the countryside was there a poorer home than the Luthers. But Martin did not mind, and as he grew rapidly into a tall thoughtful lad, he went cheerfully about his tasks, singing at the top of his voice, many times to forget his hunger.

Martin loved music and his voice was sweet and true, and whenever there was a moment to spare, off he ran to find the neighbor boys to teach them songs in parts. Then proudly to the nearby villages he led his little band, to sing at house doors in return for bread or a good hot sausage cake.

And so it is no wonder that Martin found a way to go to the choir school at Eisenach, there to sing in return for his schooling, and then on to the University of Ehrfurt, to win the highest honors. The students loved and admired the strong leader and eagerly gathered around him when he talked or played for them on his lute.

Martin loved to read and, hungering for more of the Bible after hearing bits of it read in the church, he hurried off to the library and was soon lost in wonder and delight at the beauties that he found there.

Then everyone must have this joy, he decided, and at once he set to work to write the Bible in the language of the people, so that they might have this comfort and strength to use as they wished.

And music there must be, as well; and in his own little cottage Luther worked, setting his heart stirring words to lovely old folk melodies. Then what fine times there were, trying them out at night with his neighbors and his own little ones gathered around him.

But there were sad and difficult times for Martin Luther — times when he and his followers were threatened with death for daring to worship as they chose. One day, seeing a little bird sitting on a bough of a pear tree just outside his window, he thought: that little creature—how it covers its head with its wings, and will sleep there, so still and fearless, though over it are the infinite starry spaces and the great blue depths of immensity. Yet it fears not: it is at home. God who made it, too, is there.

Comforted, he turned to his simple oaken table, and taking his pen, wrote the majestic song, "A mighty fortress is our God," not once stopping until the last word was set down.

At once the great hymn was printed, and spread through the country overnight, to be the rallying song of the people, and sung by the soldiers as they went into battle to fight for justice and truth.

And when weariness settled upon him, Luther was glad when evening came and he could sit with his little ones around him and sing away the cares of the day. "A Mighty Fortress is Our God," with its simple, rugged melody, was one of their favorite songs, and is still one of the favorites of the whole world, written for us by the courageous Martin Luther.

ROCK OF AGES

AUGUSTUS TOPLADY strode through the sunlit hills of Devon, drinking in the fresh mountain air that blew crisply from the rolling Mendip Range looming gently against the summer sky.

Now and then he stopped his joyous walking to look back at the little church, sheltered among the flowing hills. So pure and white it stood, with its slender spire pointing like a sentinel straight into the clean blue heavens.

Young pastor Toplady smiled. How good it was to be here in this beautiful English countryside, helping the mountain folk and speaking to them on Sunday in the peaceful worshipping house that they had worked so hard to build.

As he tramped along, his heart singing for joy, darkness gathered around him suddenly, and looking up in surprise, he saw that angry clouds were racing across the sun.

A mountain storm! It would break any moment now in the rocky glen of Burrington Combe, and anxiously Toplady looked about for a place of safety. The first heavy drops began to fall and scrambling over the great boulders, he rushed on, when suddenly before him arose two great pillars of rock with a ledge just large enough to crawl onto.

Clinging to the rough walls overhead, he slipped carefully into the narrow fissure and peered cautiously down to the sheer drop of rock far, far below.

He was safe now, and as the birds circled over his head with piercing cries, looking for shelter against the fiercely driving storm, words came into the young Englishman's mind. Quickly taking a bit of paper from his pocket, he wrote them down, the thunder crashing in his ears and flashes of lightning making bright his crumpled paper.

"Rock of ages, cleft for me,
Let me hide myself in Thee."

Years later, Thomas Hastings, the American writer of hymns and hymn tunes from Connecticut, came upon Toplady's poem, and liking it, set "Rock of Ages" to music, giving all the world a fine hymn to sing.

And in the early days of our country, when our brave pioneers were struggling over western mountains and plains to find new homes in the wilderness, their favorite "Rock of Ages" rang out into the starry night over their camp fires, giving strength and courage to face the hidden dangers of the morrow.

And "Rock of Ages" is still one of the favorite hymns of all mankind, giving comfort and help to all those in need.

Rock of Ages

Augustus M. Toplady

Thomas Hastings

1. Rock of A - ges, cleft for me, Let me hide my - self in Thee; Let the wa - ter and the blood, From Thy wound - ed side which flowed, Be of sin the dou - ble cure, Save from wrath and make me pure.

2. Could my tears for - ev - er flow, Could my zeal no lan - guor know, These for sin could not a - tone; Thou must save, and Thou a - lone: In my hand no price I bring; Simp - ly to Thy cross I cling.

3. While I draw this fleet - ing breath, When my eyes shall close in death, When I rise to worlds un - known, And be - hold Thee on Thy throne: Rock of A - ges, cleft for me, Let me hide my - self in Thee.

FAR across the ocean in lovely Brittany, eight hundred long years ago, there lived a wise and good monk named Bernard of Morlaix. Now Bernard's mother and father, coming from their beautiful home in England, had rested long in lovely Morlaix. It was here that their fine son, Bernard, had been born to them, there to spend joyous growing years in the fair city.

And so much of his time was spent in France, it is no wonder that when it came time to choose his life work, Bernard should journey to old Burgundy, there to become a monk and spend the rest of his days in Cluny, the finest cloister in all the French countryside.

There was never a more beautiful spot in all the wide world, and Bernard was so happy, his heart sang for joy as he wandered over the peaceful vine-covered slopes and verdant hills, a land of corn and wine, close to the fertile source of the river Seine.

Giant oakes and beeches seven long centuries old, stood like sentinels of ages gone by, and so strong were they and hoary with age, that Bernard felt blessed as he stopped to rest in their cooling shade.

Many brothers came to Cluny to worship in the peaceful stillness of the fragrant gardens. But there was special work to be done each day, and as he tended the vegetables and fruits that supplied the long wooden tables, Bernard loved to sing praises to God for the goodness of life around him.

At the first sound of the clear, pure voice, flowing like a fresh mountain stream, every back down the long rows of the garden was straightened as eager monks stopped to listen.

Old Peter, the Abbot, himself a master of song, smiled happily from his sunny corner in the arbor.

"Ah, yes," he sighed to a nearby brother, "I am growing old now, and gladly I bestow my singing hood on our blessed Bernard. Far better does he sound praises to the Lord than I."

Then, suddenly catching sight of the rows of listening monks, he added:

"Go at once, Brother, and take word to Bernard that he must keep his singing until vespers, or we shall all go hungry."

As the sun slipped behind the far-off hills and the silvery arc of a new moon sailed overhead, the brothers gathered quietly about Bernard of Morlaix, there in the cooling dusk to listen spellbound to the beauty of his song. And Bernard sang always of heaven and the glories awaiting him there.

One of the brothers, eager to capture the words, took them down carefully. And over three thousand lines there were, the only poem ever to come from the lips of Bernard.

Long years later, the musician, Alexander Ewing, choosing some of the verses translated by the Englishman, John Mason Neale, wrote music for the story of heaven. And he called the hymn, "Jerusalem, the Golden," which tells us of the fair land that Bernard liked to dream about, richly blessed with milk and honey.

Jerusalem the Golden

BERNARD OF CLUNY
Tr. JOHN MASON NEALE

ALEXANDER C. EWING

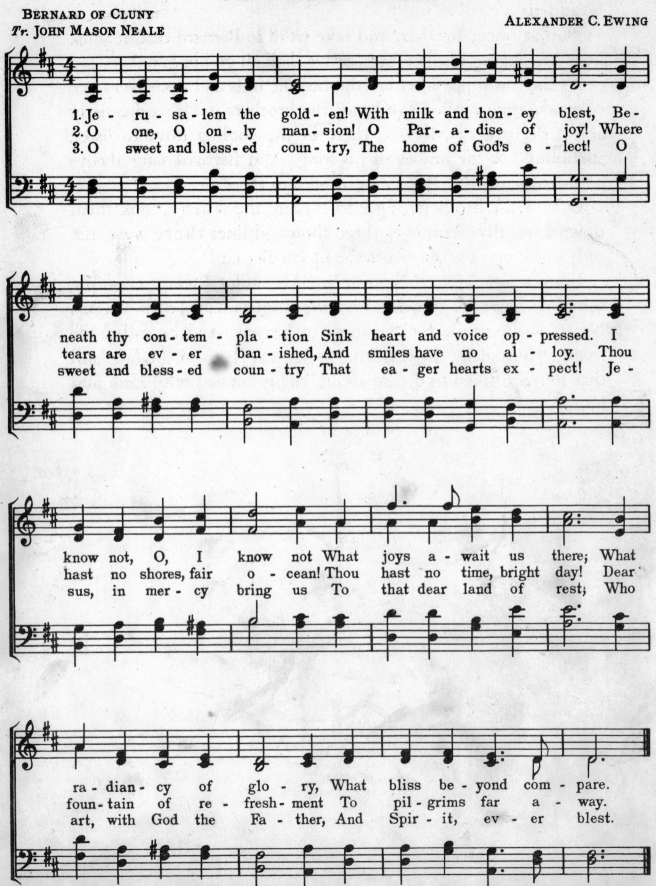

1. Je - ru - sa - lem the gold - en! With milk and hon - ey blest, Be-
2. O one, O on - ly man - sion! O Par - a - dise of joy! Where
3. O sweet and bless - ed coun - try, The home of God's e - lect! O

neath thy con - tem - pla - tion Sink heart and voice op - pressed. I
tears are ev - er ban - ished, And smiles have no al - loy. Thou
sweet and bless - ed coun - try That ea - ger hearts ex - pect! Je -

know not, O, I know not What joys a - wait us there; What
hast no shores, fair o - cean! Thou hast no time, bright day! Dear
sus, in mer - cy bring us To that dear land of rest; Who

ra - dian - cy of glo - ry, What bliss be - yond com - pare.
foun - tain of re - fresh - ment To pil - grims far a - way.
art, with God the Fa - ther, And Spir - it, ev - er blest.

ALL HAIL THE POWER OF JESUS' NAME

NO closer friends could be found in all the English country-side than the gifted young Charles Wesley and Edward Perronet. Now Charles spent much of his time in traveling from one city to another, talking to the people and telling them stories from the Bible. And wherever he went, Edward was always at his side.

He was very proud of the spirited Charles and listened closely when he spoke. And he was especially pleased with the hymns that his friend had written, that seemed never to stop coming from his magic pen, and sung everywhere by the delighted people.

So it was not surprising that before long, Edward, too, fired by his friend's words, began to speak to little groups that gathered to hear him. But never would he do so before the much admired Charles.

Now Charles was very eager to hear his friend Perronet, and waited patiently for the time to come when he would be allowed to do so. But when the weeks and months rolled by and still no word came from the young speaker, Charles decided to play a little joke on his good friend.

One bright Sunday morning, looking down at the congregation before him, he began to speak, when suddenly he spied Edward seated there comfortably, waiting to hear his words.

"My people," began Charles with a smile, "you will be very pleased to hear that from this pulpit tomorrow, the gifted young Edward Perronet will speak to you."

Edward started in his chair. To appear before Charles? But this he could not do! In despair he left for his small room, where all day and all night long he struggled for fitting words to deliver before his friend.

It was no use. Morning dawned at last, and putting aside the empty paper, off to the crowded church went the heartsick Perronet. There, in the front row sat Charles, a smile of welcome lighting his handsome face.

It was just time for the services to begin, and as Edward took his place on the platform, an idea came suddenly into his mind and at the thought, his heart leaped for joy.

"Good people," said he, "I have no sermon to give you, but I promise you a far better one than ever I could have composed for you."

Opening the Bible, he turned to the Sermon on the Mount, and in deep, mellowed tones, read the beautiful words and dismissed the people with a smile. He had indeed given them greater riches than he, himself, could have written.

Later, needing songs for the simple folk of his small country church, Edward Perronet wrote some hymns for them, patterning them after those of his friend, Charles Wesley. His beautiful "All Hail the Power of Jesus' Name," was set to several melodies, but the one most loved was written by a Massachusetts carpenter, Oliver Holden, who journeyed about the country in his spare time, leading singing schools and writing simple music for his little groups to sing.

And the small organ on which Oliver Holden first played his music of "All Hail the Power of Jesus' Name," is still proudly standing in the Old State House above the Commons, in Boston.

Queen Victoria was especially fond of this fine hymn, and whenever it was played in her presence, she directed that her jeweled crown be removed. Her power was as nothing compared to the power of Jesus' name.

All Hail the Power of Jesus' Name

EDWARD PERRONET

OLIVER HOLDEN

MY FAITH LOOKS UP TO THEE

THE bitter January wind whipped up the morning fire to a cheery blaze in the simple Massachusetts home of the Masons, and gently pulling the oaken crib to the fast reddening stove, grocer Mason strode happily away to parcel out the supplies of lard and kerosene and meal for the day.

"A new son named Lowell? Right glad to hear it, storekeeper!" greeted the customers warmly. "Good to have a sturdy lad to help around the place."

But as young Lowell grew swiftly to be a straight, handsome boy with twinkling eyes, Father Mason became more and more disturbed as he watched the deep longing that possessed the lad from sunup until nightfall, — a longing for music.

No neighbor with an instrument lived too far away for Lowell, and away he trudged across the fields, singing at the top of his voice at the thought of the riches in store for him,—long joyous hours when he would teach himself to play on the borrowed instrument.

Leaving the boy in charge of the store would no longer do, decided Father Mason, for always when he returned, there were customers outside the bolted door, while sounds of music drifted gently down from the room above.

"Music, always music," sighed storekeeper Mason. "Fiddling and singing will bring the boy to no good end, I'll be bound."

But the happiest day of his life came to Lowell late one sunny afternoon when a messenger arrived at the simple cottage, inviting him to lead the village band. Lowell was off in a flash, and from then on, there were never idle moments in the long busy years ahead, with choirs to lead and singing schools throughout the countryside to organize and conduct.

To please Father Mason, Lowell went off to Georgia to earn his living in a bank. But there was still time left in the day to lead the city choir and to learn from a fine music master how to write the melodies that were singing in his mind.

And steadily in the heart of Lowell Mason there was a growing desire to find better music for the people of America to play and sing. All that they had now were chanting plain tunes sung in the church, all out of time and tune.

Something must be done, and at once, and Lowell set to work with a will. Soon his own lovely melodies and the works of Handel and Haydn were printed with fitting words, and sent throughout the land to the grateful people. On to Boston went the tireless worker, teaching men, women, and children about music, until at last all America was singing.

One day, walking through a Boston street, he came upon the young poet, Roy Palmer.

"Ah, my good friend," greeted Mason, warmly, "I am making a book of hymns for everyone to sing. Surely you must have some verses that I could set to music."

"Verses," mused Palmer, taking a crumpled yellow paper from his pocket. "Ah yes,—here are some lines that I wrote years ago, in thankfulness for getting well from a severe illness."

Hastily reading the lines, Mason's eyes glowed. "The very thing, Palmer!" he exclaimed. "You may preach many good sermons, my friend, but this poem of yours will do more to the hearts of men than anything you may say today."

And this hymn has given more help to people the world over than these men ever dreamed, in their strong and steady, "My Faith Looks up to Thee."

My Faith Looks Up to Thee

ROY PALMER

LOWELL MASON

1. My faith looks up to Thee, Thou Lamb of Cal - va - ry, Sav - iour di - vine! Now hear me while I pray, Take all my guilt a - way, O let me from this day Be whol - ly Thine.

2. May Thy rich grace im - part Strength to my faint - ing heart, My zeal in - spire; As Thou hast died for me, O may my love to Thee Pure, warm and change - less be, A liv - ing fire!

3. While life's dark maze I tread, And griefs a - round me spread, Be Thou my guide; Bid dark - ness turn to day, Wipe sor - row's tears a - way, Nor let me ev - er stray From Thee a - side.

NOW THE DAY IS OVER

JUST one hundred years ago, in the old English city of York, there could not have been found a busier household than the Barnby's, with seven lively boys to be cared for. Poor Mother Barnby seldom found quiet moments of rest with so many mouths to be fed, and an overflowing work basket of mending always waiting to be done.

Now the youngest of the seven, slender, dark eyed Joseph, did not have time to join in the mischievous sport of his older brothers for he had his own special work to do. His father and mother watched in amusement as the small boy wrestled with the family organ, his short legs straining to reach the pedals as he played melodies with a sureness that startled his listeners.

Joseph loved to sing, too, and at the first sound of the silvery tones echoing through the house, all noise was stilled at once and everyone moved about on tiptoe, eager to catch every note of the lilting melodies.

Father Barnby decided that something should be done, and at once.

"Come, Joseph," he called early one morning, "we will visit the choir master in the church, to see what he thinks of the Barnby songbird."

The music director smiled at the eager, seven-year-old boy with eyes shining solemnly from a round, well scrubbed face. But Joseph was ready, and lifting his head, such clear pure tones went ringing through the church that the director stopped his playing to look sharply at the young performer.

"So!" he exclaimed wonderingly. "And who has taught you to sing so well, young man?"

"God, I think," answered Joseph, quietly.

Not only did Joseph enter the choir school at once, but at ten he was directing the other boys in their difficult melodies, and at twelve was given the proud position of choir master!

He was the organist, as well, playing such music as was never before heard in the church.

But Joseph decided that now it was time to go away to London to learn more about music, so off went the hard working young man, and soon beautiful melodies of his own came from his pen, to be printed for everyone to play and sing.

To the largest churches in England he went to play on the organ, and his choir singers were the finest in all the land. His orchestras, too, gave beautiful concerts for the people, and Queen Victoria, delighted with Joseph Barnby's music services to England, bestowed on him the highest honor in the land by making him a knight.

To the words written by Sabine Baring-Gould, Barnby wrote the music for one of the loveliest hymns that we have: "Now the Day is Over."

The young English writer, Baring-Gould, eager to help the poor mining people of Horbury Bridge, opened a school where they could study at night. And they must have services on Sunday; and for these simple folk whom he loved and cared for so well, he wrote the tender evening song, "Now the Day is Over", so soothing and restful, with the music of Joseph Barnby fitting the words so exactly.

Now the Day is Over

SABINE BARING-GOULD

JOSEPH BARNBY

1. Now the day is over,
2. Now the darkness gathers,
3. Jesus, give the weary
4. Grant to little children

Night is drawing nigh, Shadows of the
Stars begin to peep, Birds, and beasts, and
Calm and sweet repose; With Thy tend'rest
Visions bright of Thee, Guard the sailors

evening Steal across the sky.
flowers Soon will be asleep.
blessing May our eyelids close.
tossing On the deep blue sea.

5. Through the long night watches
   May thine angels spread
   Their white wings above me,
   Watching o'er my bed.

6. When the morning wakens
   Then may I arise,
   Pure, and fresh, and sinless
   In Thy holy eyes.

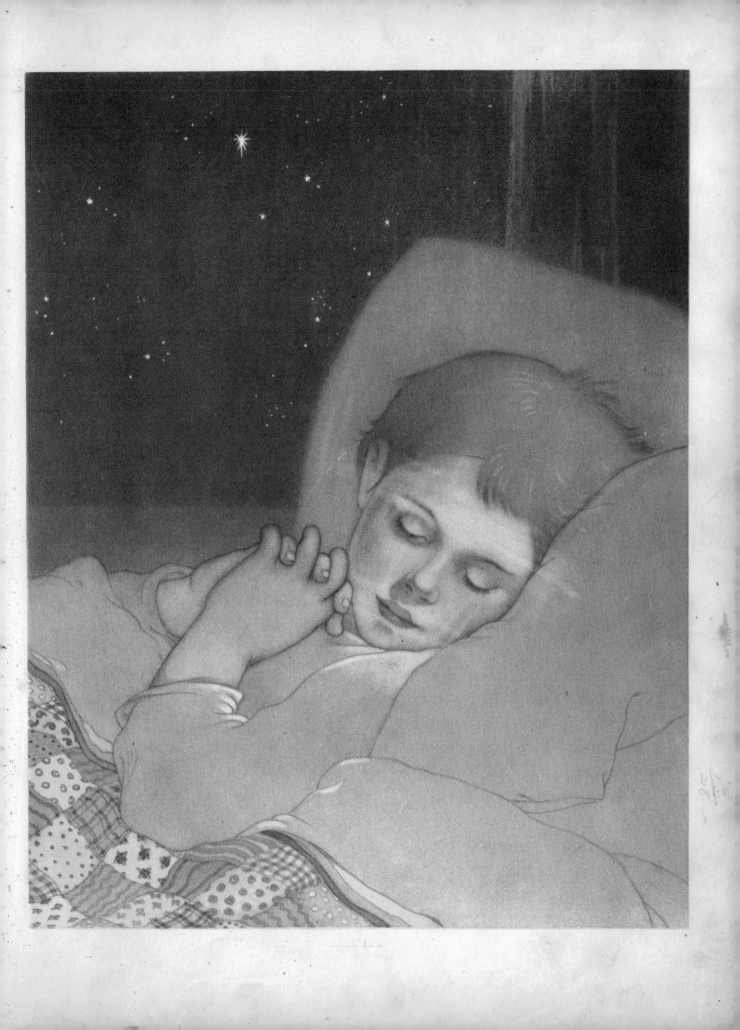

ABIDE WITH ME

EVENING was coming on, and the simple, hardly sailor folk of the little English fishing town of Brixham gathered sadly around their beloved Henry Lyte, calling their good-byes as they helped him into his shallow boat.

"Stay here with us, master Lyte. We need you," urged fisherman Dorrit, holding the light skiff steady for its frail passenger.

"Yes! Yes!" chorused the children, slipping their silvery gifts of freshly caught fish in the narrow bow. "Stay with us, master Lyte. Do not go away."

Henry Lyte looked into the honest, weather beaten faces of the toilers of the sea whom he had helped in all their troubles these twenty-four long years. If only he did not have to spend the winters in a warmer clime, there would be no need of farewells.

Patting the sun bleached heads of the children, he spoke to them gently.

"Did you know that every morning now, long before sunup, the faithful little robins have been at my window, warning me that autumn is at hand? Yes, and the busy swallows are already preparing for flight, and have invited me to go with them to the warm southland. So you see it is time now for me to leave you."

Loving cries of farewell followed him over the water as he plied his small boat along the banks of the Dart, twisting and turning by deep oaken woods and ferny slopes. On he glided, over the lovely waters and at last rounded a point under the shelter of the hills. There, peeping out of the deep green, was his rustic roof top in the dreaming stillness.

Soon he had climbed to his garden, every bush and tree and flower planted and tended by his own hands until his secret bower was a thing of rare beauty.

The sun was setting in a blaze of glory, shining warmly against the purple hills of Dartmoor. And there, just below, was the peaceful harbor of Brixham, the small boats already setting sail for the fishing grounds to spend the long, lonely night.

A warm smile lighted the kindly face of the beautiful hearted Henry Lyte. If he were near enough, he knew well that he would hear the gentle strains of the hymns that he had written for the fisher folk, sung from the decks of their venturesome little boats.

If only he could leave them something for comfort while he spent the angry months away, he could go from them with a more contented heart.

Evening was falling quickly now, and as the darkness gathered softly on leaf and tree, he made his way to his study. Seated there in the peaceful, sheltering dusk, words came suddenly into his mind and quietly he set them down: "Abide with me, fast falls the eventide."

There, it was finished,—the comforting words for his dear fisher folk, so simple and warm, later set to music by the Englishman, Henry Monk.

And not only did this beautiful hymn, "Abide With Me," comfort the fishermen of the little town of Brixham, but it has comforted people the whole world over, these hundred long years since.

Abide with Me

HENRY F. LYTE

WILLIAM H. MONK

1. A - bide with me: fast falls the e - ven - tide;
2. I need Thy pres - ence ev - 'ry pass - ing hour;

The dark - ness deep - ens; Lord, with me a - bide:
What but Thy grace can foil the tempt - er's pow'r?

When oth - er help - ers___ fail, and com - forts flee,
Who, like Thy - self, my___ guide and stay can be?

Help of the help - less, O, a - bide with me.
Through cloud and sun - shine, Lord, a - bide with me.

46

1

FAIREST LORD JESUS

(The Crusader's Hymn)

MANY, many long years ago, in countries across the sea, bands of stout hearted pilgrims left their homes to begin the endless journey on foot to the Holy Land, so eager were they to visit the place where the Christ Child had been born.

Dangers beset them on every hand, but nothing could stop their onward march as with courage undaunted, they pressed toward the land of their hearts' desire.

Even the children of two lands, believing that they had a divine mission, began long pilgrimages of their own that were to end in sad crusades, indeed.

There was Etienne, the beautiful fair haired boy of France, who arose one sunny morning over seven hundred years ago, and leaving his simple home near Vendome, called the children from their doorways as he strode valiently along.

"Come, children of God!" he cried, "On to the Holy Land!"

Three hundred thousand fair little ones obeyed his call, marching and singing behind their stalwart leader as he urged them down the rough roads of France.

Great suffering and untold hardships were to come to the brave young crusaders, but never did they arrive in the land of their dreams, and never, alas, did they find their comforting homes again.

Then there was Nicholas, the German lad, who led his band of pilgrim children across rugged mountains and vast plains into Italy, on their way to the home of Jesus.

As they marched hopefully along, their clear young voices rang triumphantly over hill and valley, the glorious, age old hymn of praise, "Fairest Lord Jesus," ever on their lips.

No one knows who wrote the words of this fair song, one of the noblest ever given to mankind. The melody is an old Silesian folk song, possibly sung by the simple peasant folk and by the shepherds on the hills as they tended their flocks by day and by night.

This lovely old tune was arranged for us by an American who also wrote the music for the carol, "It Came Upon the Midnight Clear", the Boston journalist and musician, Richard Storr Willis.

Fairest Lord Jesus
(Crusader's Hymn)

SILESIAN

1. Fair - est Lord Je - sus, Rul - er of all
2. Fair - are the mead - ows, Fair - er still the
3. Fair - is the sun - shine, Fair - er still the

na - ture, O Thou of God and__ man the Son!
wood - lands, Robed in the bloom - ing__ garb of spring;
moon - light, And all the twink - ling,__ star - ry host;

Thee will I cher - ish, Thee will I
Je - sus is fair - er, Je - sus is
Je - sus shines bright - er, Je - sus shines

hon - or, Thou, my soul's glo - ry, joy and crown.
pur - er, Who makes the woe - ful heart to sing.
pur - er, Than all the an - gels heav'n can boast.

COME, THOU ALMIGHTY KING

THERE was never a more majestic hymn, loved and sung by more people around the whole wide world these two hundred long years, than "Come, Thou Almighty King."

Although there are many who believe that the words were written by the greatest hymn writer, Charles Wesley, we are not really sure of the author.

The melody is called "The Italian Hymn," not because the music was composed in Italy, but because it was written by the Italian, Felice de' Giardini, who was not only a violinist, but a conductor and composer, as well.

While Felice de' Giardini was in Russia, playing on his violin for the great crowds of people who gathered to hear him, he set the words of "Come, Thou Almighty King," to music.

And we are glad that he gave us this stately melody so that we may go on singing this glorious song of worship all our lives long.

Come, Thou Almighty King

CHARLES WESLEY   FELICE DE GIARDINI

1. Come, Thou al - might - y King, Help us Thy
2. Come, Thou in - car - nate Word, Gird on Thy
3. Come, Ho - ly Com - fort - er, Thy sa - cred

name___ to sing; Help us to praise!
might - y sword, Our prayer at - tend!
wit - - ness bear, In this glad hour!

Fa - ther all - glo - ri - ous, O'er all vic - to - ri - ous,
Come, and Thy peo - ple bless, And give Thy word suc - cess:
Thou, who al - might - y art, Now rule in ev - 'ry heart,

Come and reign o - ver us, An - cient of days!
Spir - it of ho - li - ness, On us de - scend!
And ne'er from us de - part, Spir - it of pow'r!

BLEST BE THE TIE THAT BINDS

JOHN FAWCETT closed the doors of the small Yorkshire church where the faithful and loving village folk had listened to his words of comfort for the last time.

Hurrying to his simple home, he found all in readiness to leave for the new house in the great city of London. There stood the patient horses, ready to pull the heavily loaded wagons that were piled high over the groaning wheels with furniture and stoves and bedding and books.

One by one the poor folk gathered silently around their beloved leader, and from the doorway of the empty cottage, John Fawcett spoke to them gently.

"My good friends, it is time now to say farewell," he began kindly. "I wish we might stay here with you always, but there are too many needs for our fast growing family, and so we must be on our way to the big church in London."

Good Mother Fawcett listened quietly, looking into the saddened faces gathered around her. Then, sinking down on a packing box, she covered her face with her hands.

"Oh, John, John," she cried, "I cannot bear this. I know not how to go."

Quietly her husband sat beside her, and for long minutes was lost in anxious thought. Suddenly a light came into his eyes and he arose briskly.

"Nor will we go," he announced firmly, "unload the wagons, all hands. Here we shall stay."

With joyous shouts the village folk set to work with a will, and so soon was every book and simple piece of furniture back in its proper place, that no one could could have told that they had ever been moved!

At once a warm peace settled in the heart of John Fawcett, and a few days later, deeply touched by the joy and gratitude of the country folk, he sat to write the lines of a poem that came singing in his mind:

"Blest be the tie that binds
Our hearts in Christian love."

The simple, meaningful words were set to a gentle, lilting melody by Hans George Nageli, a Zurich musician, the tune later changed a little by our own American composer, Lowell Mason.

And so for these two hundred long years, people everywhere have had this simple, beautiful song of kinship to sing and enjoy.

Blest Be the Tie That Binds

JOHN FAWCETT   HANS G. NAGELI

Children of the Heavenly King

JOHN CENNICK

IGNACE J. PLEYEL

1. Chil - dren of the heav'n - ly King,
2. We - are trav - 'ling home to God
3. Lord, o - be - dient - ly we'll go,

As we jour - ney let us sing;
In the way our fa - thers trod;
Glad - ly leav - ing all be - low,

Sing our Sa - viour's worth - y praise,
They are hap - py now and we
On - ly Thou our lead - er be,

Glo - rious in his works and ways.
Soon their hap - pi - ness shall see.
And we still will fol - low Thee.

Saviour, Teach Me, Day by Day

JANE E. LEESON

LEIGHTON G. HAYNE

1. Sa - viour, teach me, day by day, Love's sweet les - son to o - bey; Sweet - er les - son can - not be, Lov - ing Him Who first loved me.
2. With a child - like heart of love, At Thy bid - ding may I move; Prompt to serve and fol - low Thee, Lov - ing Him Who first loved me.
3. Teach me all Thy steps to trace, Strong to fol - low in Thy grace; Learn - ing how to love from Thee, Lov - ing Him Who first loved me.

Heavenly Father, Send Thy Blessing

UNKNOWN

JEAN JACQUES ROUSSEAU

1. Heav'n-ly Fa-ther, send Thy bless-ing On Thy chil-dren gath-er'd here; May they all, Thy Name con-fess-ing Be to Thee for ev-er dear: May they be, like Jo-seph, lov-ing, Du-ti-ful, and chaste, and pure; And their faith, like Da-vid, prov-ing, Stead-fast un-to death en-dure.

2. Ho-ly Sav-iour, Who in meek-ness Didst vouch-safe a Child to be, Guide their steps, and help their weak-ness Bless and make them like to Thee; Bear Thy lambs, when they are wear-y, In Thine Arms and at Thy Breast; Through life's des-ert, dry and drear-y, Bring them to Thy heav'n-ly rest.

3. Spread Thy gold-en pin-ions o'er them, Ho-ly Spir-it, from a-bove, Guide them, lead them, go be-fore them, Give them peace, and joy, and love: Thy true tem-ples, Ho-ly Spir-it, May they with Thy glo-ry shine, And im-mor-tal bliss in-her-it, And for ev-er-more be Thine.

64

Jesus, Tender Shepherd, Hear Me

MARY DUNCAN

CHARLOTTE A. BARNARD

1. Je - sus, ten - der Shep - herd, hear me;
2. All this day Thy hand has led me,
3. Let my sins be all for - giv - en;

Bless Thy lit - tle lamb to - night:
And I thank Thee for Thy care;
Bless the friends I love so well:

Through the dark - ness be Thou near me;
Thou hast warm'd me, cloth'd and fed me;
Take us all at last to heav - en,

Keep me safe till morn - ing light.
Lis - ten to my eve - ning pray'r!
Hap - py there with Thee to dwell.

I Think When I Read That Sweet Story

JEMIMA LUKE

ENGLISH

1. I think when I read that sweet story of old, When Jesus was here among men, How He call'd little children as lambs to His fold: I should like to have been with Him then.

2. I wish that His hands had been placed on my head, That His arms had been thrown around me, And that I might have seen His kind look when He said: "Let the little ones come unto Me."

3. Yet still to His footstool in pray'r I may go And may ask for a share in His love; And if thus I shall earnestly seek Him below, I shall see Him and hear Him above.

4. In that beautiful place He has gone to prepare For all who are wash'd and forgiv'n; And many dear children are gathering there, For of such is the Kingdom of Heav'n.

Morning Thanks

John Pierpont

Westphalian Tune

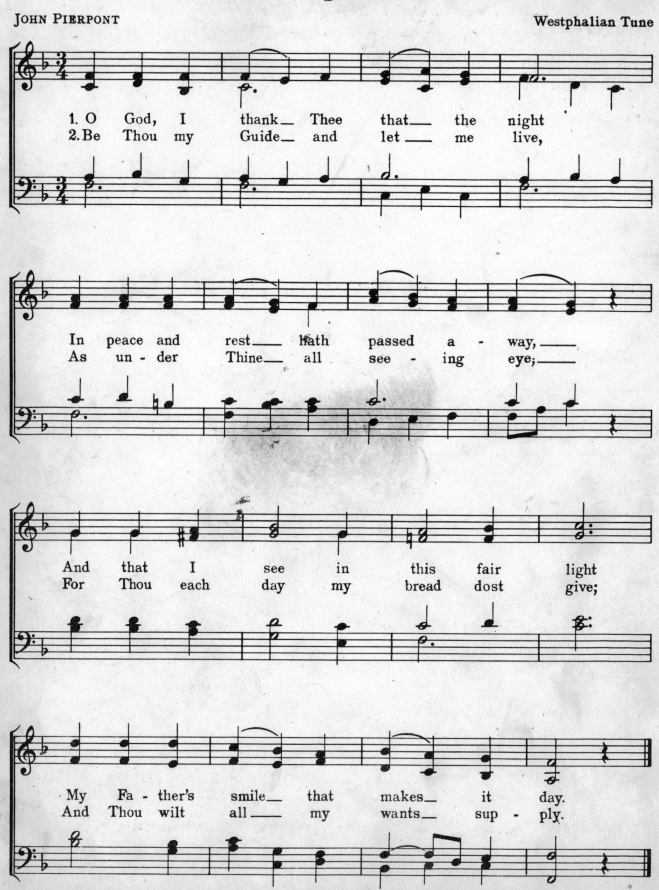

1. O God, I thank_ Thee that_ the night
2. Be Thou my Guide_ and let_ me live,

In peace and rest_ hath passed a - way,_
As un - der Thine_ all see - ing eye;_

And that I see in this fair light
For Thou each day my bread dost give;

My Fa - ther's smile_ that makes_ it day.
And Thou wilt all_ my wants_ sup - ply.

Dear Lord and Father of Mankind

JOHN G. WHITTIER

FREDERICK C. MAKER

1. Dear Lord and Fa-ther of man-kind, For-
2. In sim-ple trust like theirs who heard, Be-
3. O Sab-bath rest by Ga-li-lee! O
4. Drop Thy still dews of qui-et-ness, Till
5. Breathe through the heats of our de-sire Thy

give our fool-ish ways! Re-clothe us in our
side the Sy-rian Sea, The gra-cious call-ing
calm of hills a-bove, Where Je-sus knelt to
all our striv-ings cease: Take from our souls the
cool-ness and Thy balm; Let sense be dumb, let

right-ful mind, In pur-er lives Thy
of the Lord, Let us, like them, with-
share with Thee The si-lence of e-
strain and stress, And let our or-dered
flesh re-tire; Speak through the earth-quake,

ser-vice find, In deep-er rev-'rence, praise.
out a word, Rise up and fol-low Thee.
ter-ni-ty In-ter-pre-ted by love.
lives con-fess The beau-ty of Thy peace.
wind and fire, O still, small voice of calm.

DEAR LORD AND FATHER OF MANKIND

THE Whittier household lay half buried under the great drifts of snow that had been piling steadily under the eaves through the long dark night.

Small John was up with the dawn, racing upstairs and down, flattening his eager nose against the frosty panes, and scratching peepholes in the lacy ice-patterned windows, to catch a glimpse of the whirling white wonder world outside.

"We're prisoners, Mother!" he shouted from the landing, "snow prisoners in our own house."

Around the wide throated chimney, the shut in family gathered to hear the boarding schoolmaster play happy and mournful tunes on his fiddle, as the firelight danced on whitewashed walls and sagging beams. John's eyes grew wide, and chills ran down his back as witch and ghost stories went round. And to the clicking of her knitting needles, Mother Whittier told of the days when fierce Indian hordes rushed down on Cocheco Town in the stillness of midnight.

"Nine o'clock and time for bed," she finished quietly, her gentle prayer blessing the bowed heads of her dear ones: "We thank Thee, Lord, for health and home and food and loving care. Guard us through another night. Amen."

In his bed, John shivered beside his older brother at the sound of the sea crashing outside, and the icy wind rocking the very bedstead where he lay.

"Do you hear them, brother?" he whispered. "They're white-sheeted ghosts, riding high against the storm." There was no answer, and soon he, too, was lost in whirling dreams.

In these shut in days, how treasured were the few books on the shelf,—the Bible, the almanac, and an old worn copy of the Scotch poet, Burns. Eagerly John feasted on the homely singing lines, learning many of them by heart that were to be his life-long joy.

John loved his simple Quaker farm home in the gray hills of the beautiful Merrimac Valley. There he played hard and worked hard, each year spending a few months at school in the small red building close by.

Quietly he saved what little money he earned, and was proud and happy on the day when there was enough to take him away to a higher school for two whole years.

But always, deep in his mind there were forming word pictures of the joys and labors of the simple New England folk about him. And so it is no wonder that splendid poems, books of them, should one day come from his pen, to be eagerly read throughout the land.

And when slavery came to molest the country, pages came flooding from his troubled heart, helping to set the slave men free.

And from the kindly pen of our beloved New England poet, John Greenleaf Whittier, came an urgent prayer: "Dear Lord and Father of mankind, forgive our foolish ways."

The very beautiful and simple verses were set to music by the English musician, Charles Maker, giving us such a tender, restful prayer in melody that in singing it we are refreshed, and grateful to those who have given us such a bountiful treasure.

Christ the Lord Is Risen To-day

CHARLES WESLEY

LYRA DAVIDICA

1. Christ the Lord is ris'n to-day,
2. Lives a-gain our glo-rious King;
3. Soar we now where Christ has led,
} Hal - - le - lu - jah!

Sons of men and an-gels say:
Where, O death, is now thy sting?
Fol-low our ex-alt-ed Head;
} Hal - - le - lu - jah!

Raise your joys and tri-umphs high,
Once he died our souls to save;
Made like Him, like Him we rise;
} Hal - - le - lu - jah!

Sing, ye heav'ns, and earth re-ply,
Where thy vic-t'ry boast-ing grave?
Ours the cross, the grave, the skies!
} Hal - - le - lu - jah!

CHRIST, THE LORD, IS RISEN TODAY

ALMOST two hundred and fifty years ago, in the rambling Lincolnshire home of the Wesleys, there was never an idle moment for Mother Wesley with so many merry, eager eyed children to be cared for through the long hours of each day.

And when on a foggy morning in early December, the eighteenth son arrived, her cares were never ending, and the old rectory was filled to overflowing with boys, boys, and still more boys.

But the new little son, Charles, soon won his way into everyone's heart with his sweet, serious ways, looking long and questioningly at whoever came near him with his large, deep brown eyes.

Early one morning, just as the household was waking from sleep, the smell of smoke spread swiftly through the rooms. A fire! Terror struck at the heart of Mother Wesley as she darted through the passageways, calling the children after her.

Safely outside with her excited brood, Mother Wesley counted heads anxiously. Little Charles was still missing! But the faithful old nurse was already on her way, and pushing through the blinding smoke, she rolled her favorite child in a heavy blanket and carried him safely to his cheering family.

Young Charles grew rapidly and each morning spent long hours with Mother Wesley, learning many wonderful things that he was to remember all his life long. And very early, too, he learned to struggle for himself, earning what he could for a new coat or a sturdy pair of shoes.

And so a great temptation was to come to him when his uncle Charles arrived from Ireland one fine day, offering him great riches and broad acres to rule if he would go home with the proud landowner to live as his son.

It did not take young Charles long to decide, and when the holiday season at the Westminster School came round, off to Lincolnshire he raced as fast as he could go, to spend the merriest Christmas he had ever known in his own dear home.

When he grew to be a young man, the happiest days of his life came to him when he spoke to the people in the churches of England. And there must be music in the services for the people to sing, and for them he wrote poems and set them to music, as hymns.

Most of his thoughts poured out in verse, and wherever he happened to be—on horseback or in his study, eating his dinner, or walking by the sea, the poems kept coming, and always Charles set them down.

Most of the verses were set to music, and so many of these beautiful songs came from his pen, over six thousand of them, that Charles Wesley came to be known as the greatest hymn writer of all ages.

To the whole world he gave the splendid "Jesus, Lover of My Soul," "Love Divine, All Love Excelling," "Hark, the Herald Angels Sing," and one of the most glorious and truly exultant Easter songs ever written: "Christ, the Lord is Risen Today," set to the old Latin hymn tune, Lyria Davidica.

TORREY

DUSK was softly closing in on the little Welsh town of Wrexham, and kindly Dr. Shipley turned up his study light so that he might better see the faces of the faithful neighbor folk who had come in to keep him company.

Just as the flame turned the room to cheery brightness, the door opened and there stood Reginald Heber, a happy smile lighting his gentle brown eyes. A cry of welcome sprang from the lips of good pastor Shipley as he hurried to the door.

"Reginald! Come in, son. What a gladsome sight for these old eyes of mine, waiting and watching through the long day for your coming." And into the circle of friends the little minister led his beloved son-in-law, boasting of his talents the while.

"Yes, yes, always a poet was Reginald. Why, at Oxford, and only seventeen, mind you, he took the Chancellor's prize for the best Latin poem. And just two years later, he won first place with his English verses."

Reginald smiled broadly. "Come, come, Father Shipley," he declared laughingly, "you would have me spend all of my time at poetry, and then who would care for my little church in Hodnet?"

But Dr. Shipley had not heard the last words. Turning eagerly to Reginald, he grasped his arm.

"Why not try your powers this very night, young man?" he challenged. "We badly need a new song for the services tomorrow. Come, you shall write one for us this minute!"

There was nothing to do but obey the command, and finding pen and paper at the far end of the room, Reginald began to write at once. Twenty minutes raced by, when Dr. Shipley's hearty voice interrupted him.

"Time's up, Reginald," he called, "read us your poem."

In a gentle, musical voice, the young English pastor began to read the lines that he had written:

From Greenland's icy mountains,
From India's coral strand,
Where Afric's sunny fountains
Roll down the golden sand."

There were happy exclamations from the little group.

"It is fine, Reginald! Perfect!" cried William Shipley, his face wreathed in proud smiles.

"A few more lines and it will be finished," declared Heber. And reaching for his pen, he swiftly put down the last verses.

"Come, son, give me the paper, or your fine poem will be spoiled with too many words," called Dr. Shipley, hurriedly taking the precious verses under his watchful care.

That very evening the poem was sent off to be printed, and the very next day it was sung in the parish church by the delighted people. "From Greenland's Icy Mountains" had come to stay.

The verses found their way to America, and Lowell Mason set them to a new melody, giving us this fine hymn that is sung over the wide world, the stirring "From Greenland's Icy Mountains."

From Greenland's Icy Mountains

REGINALD HEBER

LOWELL MASON

1. From Green-land's i - cy moun-tains, From In - dia's cor - al strand,
2. What though the spi - cy breez - es Blow soft o'er Cey-lon's isle,—
3. Shall we, whose souls are light - ed With wis - dom from on high,—
4. Waft, waft, ye winds, His sto - ry, And you, ye wa - ters, roll,—

Where Af - ric's sun - ny foun-tains Roll down the gold - en sand,
Though ev - 'ry pros-pect pleas - es And on - ly man is vile;
Shall we to men be - night - ed The lamp of life de - ny?
Till, like a sea of glo - ry, It spreads from pole to pole;

From many an an - cient riv - er, From many a palm - y plain,—
In vain, with lav - ish kind-ness, The gifts of God are strown:
Sal - va - tion, O sal - va - tion! The joy - ful sound pro - claim,—
Till o'er our ran-somed na - ture The Lamb, for sin - ners slain,—

They call us to de - liv - er Their land from er - ror's chain.
The heath - en in his blind-ness Bows down to wood and stone.
Till earth's re - mot - est na - tion Has learned Mes - si - ah's name.
The might - y King and Sav - iour, In bliss re - turns to reign.

NEARER, MY GOD, TO THEE

LONG, long years ago, when Isaac had grown old and weary, and blindness had settled upon him, he called his son, Jacob, to him and blessed him.

"The time has come for you to seek a fair maiden, that your home may be built sound and well," said he. "Arise, and get you to Padan-aram, there to choose a beautiful daughter of Laban. And may the blessing of Abraham be upon you, that you may inherit his land."

Fastening his sturdy sandals on securely, Jacob took meat and drink and started out for the land of Abraham. Long hours he traveled swiftly over the ground, light hearted and joyous as the birds that flew over his head.

When the clear western sky was jeweled with gleaming stars, he stopped beneath a friendly tree to rest and, weary with his journeying, stretched out on the good earth, a flat stone under his dark head for a pillow.

Smiling up at the stars so shelteringly close, his eyelids grew heavier with the passing moments and quietly closed in sleep.

And lo, the most wonderful dream unfolded itself to Jacob. Before his startled eyes was a giant ladder, stretching up, up, and on through the misty blue to the very gates of heaven. And treading lightly up and down were angels fair, their faces radiant with light as they sang their songs of joy.

At the top of the ladder stood the Master of all, in raiment so pure that Jacob could scarce look upon it, so filled with wonder was he. And gently the Master spoke to him.

"I am the Lord God of Abraham, thy Father, and the God of Isaac. The land whereon thou liest, to thee will I give it."

And Jacob awakened out of his sleep, joyous in remembrance of the glowing ladder.

"Surely the Lord was in this place," he cried, "and I knew it not!"

Springing to his feet, he poured oil upon the stone where his head had rested, and he called the place Bethel, the House of God.

Now an English woman, Sarah Flower Adams, loving the story of Jacob's fair ladder with angels climbing ever closer to God, wrote a poem which she called "Nearer, My God, to Thee."

Later, her verses were set to music. But the melody most often sung is by our American, Lowell Mason, which he based on the lovely old Irish ballad tune, "Oft in the stilly night."

Little did Sarah Adams know when she wrote it, that the hymn, "Nearer, My God, to Thee," would be sung around the world these many long years by grateful people of every race and tongue.

Nearer, My God, to Thee

SARAH F. ADAMS

LOWELL MASON

1. Near - er, my God, to Thee, Near - er to Thee! E'en though it be a cross That rais - eth me; Still all my song shall be, Near - er, my God, to Thee, Near - er, my God, to Thee, Near - er to Thee!

2. Though like the wan - der - er, The sun goes down, Dark - ness be o - ver me, My rest a stone; Yet in my dreams I'd be Near - er, my God, to Thee, Near - er, my God, to Thee, Near - er to Thee!

3. There let the way ap - pear, Steps un - to heav'n, All that Thou send - est me, In mer - cy giv'n; An - gels to beck - on me Near - er, my God, to Thee, Near - er, my God, to Thee, Near - er to Thee!

4. Then, with my wak - ing thoughts Bright with Thy praise, Out of my sto - ny griefs Beth - el I'll raise; So by my woes to be Near - er, my God, to Thee, Near - er, my God, to Thee, Near - er to Thee!

THE blustering March wind whirled around the busy docks of Hull and went racing up the half darkened English streets to the home of banker Dykes, where a plump little dark eyed boy had been born in the early dawn.

Bundled warmly in woolen blankets, he wept lustily in the arms of his proud parent.

"There now, small John,—it looks as though you would be a good singer some day, like your father," chuckled happy banker Dykes.

And that is just what happened, and as he grew swiftly to be a sturdy, good natured boy, John loved music dearly and sang heartily whenever anyone would stop to hear him. And he liked especially to listen to handsome Father Dykes, and was proudly at his side when he sang at musicals in the city.

The biggest event in all the year was the grand festival held in Trinity Church, and every morning early, John sped with all haste to the building, to sit happily through the long hours of practicing.

One day, the women were having a difficult time in singing their parts, when suddenly they spied the eager young John, his short legs swinging in time to the accompaniment. In a moment he was smuggled behind them in the choir loft, and the music began again, this time ringing out so clearly and triumphantly that the director listened in astonishment.

Then a knowing smile softened his stern face as he brought the singing to a sudden close.

"Come out, young John Dykes!" he called sharply. "The ladies must do their work alone."

John liked to amuse the household by giving concerts every evening, playing easily by ear on any instrument that he could find. But learn to read by note he must, decided Father Dykes, and in the long weeks and months that followed, he was kept sternly at his task until at last nothing was too difficult for him to play.

Now he had won his cherished goal, for his grandfather, the organist at St. John's, would allow him to play on the great instrument. Off to the church raced the young musician, and climbing joyously to the high bench, he put his hands on the keys and his glowing melodies rang through the building.

Nothing could keep him away from the organ now, and hiring his younger sisters as organ blowers at a half penny an hour, John practiced on the old instrument as long as his money lasted. Often the mischievous girls, weary with their work, stopped to rest, and instantly a deep silence settled over the church.

In great distress, John's anxious round face appeared at the small door leading to the blowers.

"Oh, my sisters," he cried, "Give me air, or my music perishes!"

Very soon the young organist was playing for the services in the church, and in amazement the audience watched the ten-year-old boy sitting high in the organ loft, straining to reach the pedals as he played beautiful music for them to enjoy.

John was sad, indeed, when it was time to move away from Hull. But he was proud and delighted when the people of the church gave him a handsome gold watch for playing so well on their organ.

And John Dyke's music never stopped, and when he grew to be a man, he became a fine musician, writing many compositions to be used in the church. Over three hundred fine hymn tunes came from his pen, among them "Lead, Kindly Light," and the moving "Holy, Holy, Holy," that we love to sing, with words written by the Englishman, Reginald Heber.

Holy, Holy, Holy!

REGINALD HEBER   JOHN B. DYKES

1. Ho - ly, Ho - ly, Ho - ly!__ Lord__ God Al - might - y!
2. Ho - ly, Ho - ly, Ho - ly!__ All the saints a - dore Thee,
3. Ho - ly, Ho - ly, Ho - ly!__ though the dark - ness hide Thee,
4. Ho - ly, Ho - ly, Ho - ly!__ Lord__ God Al - might - y!

Ear - ly in the morn - ing our song shall rise to Thee;
Cast - ing down their gold - en crowns a - round the glass - y sea;
Though the eye of sin - ful man Thy glo - ry may not see,
All Thy works shall praise Thy Name, in earth, and sky and sea;

Ho - ly, Ho - ly, Ho - ly!__ mer - ci - ful and might - y!
Cher - u - bim and ser - a - phim__ fall - ing down be - fore Thee,
On - ly Thou art ho - ly;__ there is none be - side Thee,
Ho - ly, Ho - ly, Ho - ly!__ mer - ci - ful and might - y!

God in Three Per - sons,__ bless - ed Trin - i - ty.
Which wert, and art, and__ ev - er more shalt be.
Per - fect in pow'r, in__ love, and pur - i - ty.
God in Three Per - sons,__ bless - ed Trin - i - ty!

IN the humble Austrian peasant cottage of Matthias Haydn, the wheelwright, there lived the lively little Johann Michael and his older brother, Joseph, with their simple, hard working parents.

Of all the people in his small world, Michael loved his brother Joseph, the most, and begged to be with him night and day. And never ending fun there was for the two boys, with the market square just at the end of the cobbled street, and the River Leitha hard by, where they could go fishing and sail their homemade boats from its marshy shores.

But the good times were suddenly to end, and the loneliest day of his life came to Michael when Joseph went away to live with his uncle, to learn about music.

For a long time nothing could make him happy, not even the concerts that he loved so well, when the neighbors gathered around the hearth in the low ceilinged cottage to play and sing together old Croatian folk songs.

Michael, too, sang sweetly and clearly, and on the day when the messenger brought word that he would leave at once for the great city of Vienna, to sing in the cathedral with his brother Joseph, his heart bounded for joy.

But sadness was to come to him again, for Joseph's voice began to change and the Empress did not like to listen to his solos. This meant that soon he would no longer be needed in the choir, and Michael would have to go on living at the school without him.

The Empress Maria Theresa was delighted with the fresh young voice of Michael, and to him she gave a fine present of a silken purse, heavy with silver coins.

"And what will you do with the money, Michael?" asked the stern choir director, Herr Reutter.

"Oh, I will send half to my poor father, and keep the other half until my voice breaks," answered the young soloist, thoughtfully.

Michael worked hard, indeed, and his dearest wish came true when at last he became a musician like his older brother, Joseph. He had learned to write music, too, and when he was invited to go to the beautiful city of Salzburg to be the organist and choir director there, he wrote many lovely compositions for the services in the church.

Joseph Haydn, now a famous composer, was very proud of his brother Michael, and hearing his fine church music, declared that it was far better than his own.

In lovely Salzburg there lived the noted composer Mozart, and quickly he came to know the church organist and the two became close friends. Wolfgang was very kind to Michael, sometimes writing compositions for him when he was ill, so that his small salary would not be stopped.

For the poem, "O Worship the King" written by the English lawyer, Sir Arthur Grant, who liked to make sacred verses in his spare moments, Johann Michael Haydn composed music.

Together, they have given us one of the finest songs that we have today,—the simple, majestic hymn, "O Worship the King."

O Worship the King

ROBERT GRANT

JOHANN MICHAEL HAYDN

1. O wor-ship the King, all-glo-rious a-bove! O grate-ful-ly sing His pow'r and His love; Our Shield and De-fend-er, the An-cient of days, Pa-vil-ioned in splen-dor, and gird-ed with praise.

2. O tell of His might, O sing of His grace, Whose robe is the light, whose can-o-py space; His char-iots of wrath the deep thun-der-clouds form, And dark is His path on the wings of the storm.

3. Thy boun-ti-ful care what tongue can re-cite? It breathes in the air, it shines in the light, It streams from the hills, it de-scends to the plain, And sweet-ly dis-tills in the dew and the rain.

4. Frail chil-dren of dust, and fee-ble as frail In Thee do we trust, nor find Thee to fail; Thy mer-cies, how ten-der! how firm to the end! Our Mak-er, De-fend-er, Re-deem-er, and Friend.

94